THE ENGLISH WORKBOOK

D

DEVELOPING LITERACY

Speaking

Narrative

Procedure

Recount

Writing

Report

Grammar

Exposition

Listening

Editing

Vocabulary

Spelling

Reading

Diane Henderson   Rosemary Morris

Prim-Ed
Publishing

The English workbook *(Book B)*

Published by Prim-Ed Publishing 2013
Reprinted 2015

Copyright© Diane Henderson and Rosemary Morris 2012

ISBN 978-1-84654-640-2
PR–6354

Titles available in this series:
The English workbook *(Book A)*
The English workbook *(Book B)*
The English workbook *(Book C)*
The English workbook *(Book D)*
The English workbook *(Book E)*
The English workbook *(Book F)*
The English workbook *(Book G)*

Introduction

This workbook will help you to understand procedures, recounts, expositions, narratives and reports, and to learn how to plan and write them yourself.

You will be:

- reading
- doing some comprehension
- doing some vocabulary, spelling, punctuation and grammar
- practising writing
- checking your writing
- doing a test.

Remember: *Good writers need to think about, plan and check their writing; it doesn't just happen.*

Contents

Contents

Contents

Playing hopscotch

This procedure tells us how to do something.

Read the rules.

How to play hopscotch

Equipment:
chalk, an even surface, stones

Steps:

1. Take turns.

2. Throw your stone into square 1.

3. Hop with one foot into each square (miss the square with the stone).

4. Jump into squares 4 and 5, and 8 and 9, with one foot in each square.

5. Jump and turn at squares 8 and 9.

6. Pick up your stone on the way back.

7. Throw the stone into square 2 and continue.

Note:

• This game can be played by two to five players.

• Miss a turn if a body part touches the line or your stone misses the square.

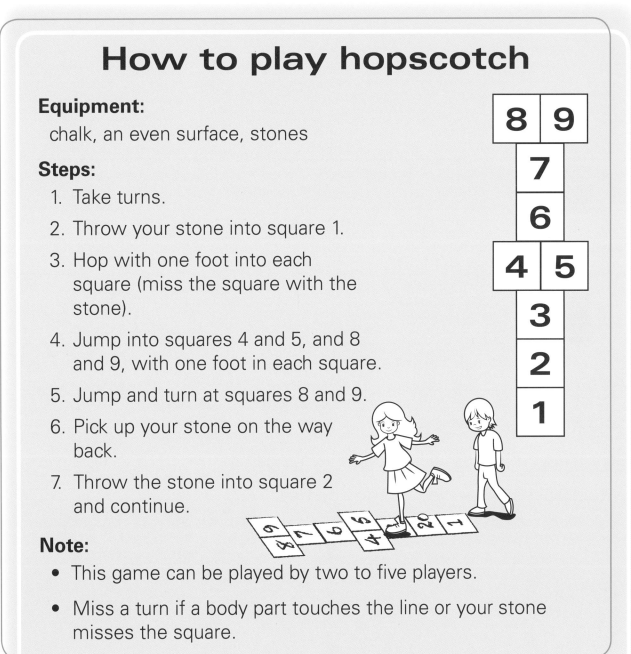

Test: Were you able to play the game?

With your class

Hopscotch is a game for two to five players.

- Make a list of other games for two to five players.
- Draw your favourite.

With a partner

Tell your partner about the game you drew.

Listen while your partner talks about his/her game.

Draw two places where you can play games.

Use the procedure on page 1 to complete the page.

1. TITLE: _____

GOAL:

2. The procedure tells you how to _____.

NEEDS:

3. Draw and label the things you will need.

STEPS:

4. How many steps are there? [ ]

5. Write the words used at the beginning of the steps.

    1. _____

    2. _____

    3. _____

    4. _____

    5. _____

    6. _____

    7. _____

6. These words are all v_____ (doing words).

TEST:

7. How would you know if the procedure was right?

_____

Read

1. Answer **yes** or **no**. Colour the box.

    (a) Two to five players can play.   yes   no

    (b) Each player has a ball.   yes   no

    (c) The grid has nine squares.   yes   no

    (d) You can put your foot on the line.   yes   no

Read and think

1. (a) Do you think hopscotch is an easy game to play? _____

    (b) Give one reason why. _____

    _____

2. Draw and label three games young children may enjoy playing.

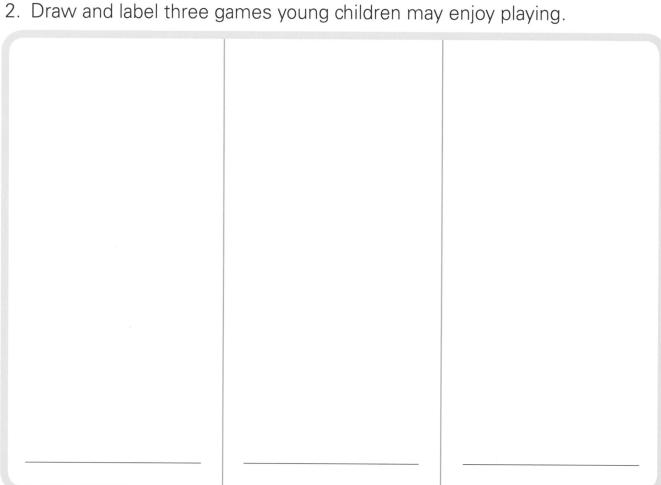

Think

1. Join the games and sports to the things you need.

skipping •

tennis •

football •

swimming •

cricket •

hockey •

high jump •

baseball •

cycling •

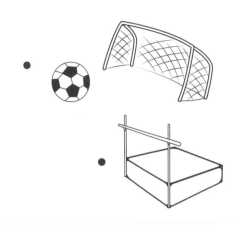

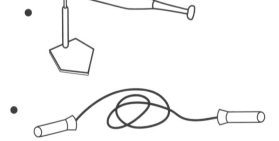

All about words

1. Look at the funny pictures and choose the right letter to put in the box.

    (a) Hide and seek

    (b) Leapfrog

    (c) Musical chairs

    (d) Drop the hanky

    (e) Duck, duck, goose

    (f) I spy

    (g) Pass the parcel

    (h) Follow the leader

    (i) Egg and spoon race

2. Join the two halves to make a game.

snakes •   • seek

noughts •   • robbers

hide •      • cold

cat •   • mouse

cops •   • crosses

hot •   • ladders

Write your favourite one. _____

3. Sort out the jumbled sports. Use the pictures for a clue.

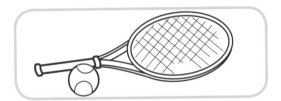

(a) nisten _____

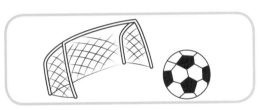

(b) loobftla _____

(c) astbblaekl _____

(d) rnuignn _____

(e) ginwimsm _____

(f) ockeyh _____

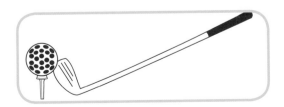

(g) olfg _____

(h) gowrni _____

Tricky words

Some words are hard to spell. They can't be sounded out. They need to be practised.

1. Look at the 10 words.
   Say each word slowly.
   Underline the tricky part.
   Learn the word.
   Cover the word.
   Practise writing the word.

	1st try	**2nd try**
the		
they		
them		
was		
were		
you		
your		
said		
one		
two		

2. These tricky words are backwards. Write them correctly.

   (a) ksa _____

   (b) ecno _____

   (c) tnaw _____

   (d) htob _____

   (e) pleh _____

   (f) sih _____

   (g) reh _____

   (h) evig _____

3. Spelling maths

tricky word	+	letter	= tricky word _____

(a) **you** + **r** = _____

(b) **the** + **y** = _____

(c) **n** + **one** = _____

(d) **d** + **one** = _____

(e) **t** + **here** = _____

(f) **t** + **his** = _____

(g) **w** + **here** = _____

(h) **m** + **any** = _____

Question words

Words that ask questions are sometimes tricky to spell.

Note: Many start with **wh**.

4. Use a **wh** word to finish the question.

(a) _____ is away today?

(b) _____ book is yours?

(c) _____ is your name?

(d) _____ did you do that?

(e) _____ do you live?

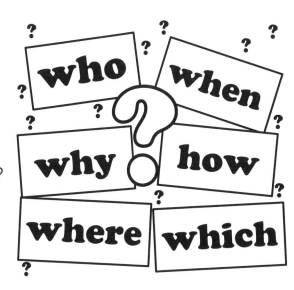

Note: **How** also has a **w** and **h** in it.

Verbs

Verbs are doing words. They describe an action.

 run    hop    skip    jump

1. Finish the verbs from the procedure on page 1.

   (a) Ta _____   (b) Th _____

   (c) H _____   (d) J _____

   (e) P _____   (f) M _____

Adverbs

Adverbs can add to the verb. They tell us more about the action.

Adverbs often end in **ly**.

2. Choose a good adverb from the box for each verb.

   | quickly   neatly   softly   down   slowly   up |

   (a) Walk _____   (b) Run _____

   (c) Reach _____   (d) Look _____

   (e) Talk _____   (f) Write _____

3. Join the opposite adverbs.

   quickly •   • carelessly

   heavily •   • loudly

   softly •   • sadly

   happily •   • lightly

   carefully •   • slowly

1. Plan a procedure.

TITLE: _____

GOAL:

   To learn how to skip.

NEEDS:

STEPS: Put your steps in order.

1. _____
   _____

2. _____
   _____

3. _____
   _____

4. _____
   _____

5. _____
   _____

TEST: How would you know if the procedure was right?

2. Check your work.

After you finish writing, check these things to make your work better.

Writing

Has your procedure got a name? .... ○ **yes** ○ **no**

Does it make sense? .... ○ **yes** ○ **no**

Did you leave out any words? .... ○ **yes** ○ **no**

Are the steps easy to understand? .... ○ **yes** ○ **no**

Are the steps in the right order? .... ○ **yes** ○ **no**

Spelling

Did you check your spelling? .... ○ **yes** ○ **no**

Words

Is there a verb in every step? .... ○ **yes** ○ **no**

Punctuation

Did you put a capital letter at the start of every
sentence? .... ○ **yes** ○ **no**

Did you remember full stops? .... ○ **yes** ○ **no**

1. These tricky words are backwards. Write them correctly.

    (a) uoy _____   (b) yeht _____

    (c) ynam _____   (d) pleh _____

2. Spelling maths

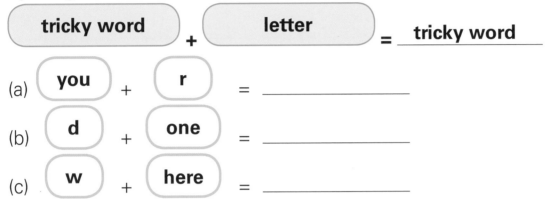

| tricky word | + | letter | = | tricky word |

    (a) **you** + **r** = _____

    (b) **d** + **one** = _____

    (c) **w** + **here** = _____

3. Use a **wh** word to finish the question.

    (a) _____ do you live?   (b) _____ is your friend?

    (c) _____ is his name?   (d) _____ are you sad?

4. Choose an adverb from the box for each verb.

    | **carefully** | **nicely** | **high** |

    (a) Listen _____   (b) Jump _____

    (c) Eat _____

5. Join the opposite adverbs.

    quickly •   • lightly

    heavily •   • slowly

    happily •   • sadly

6. Use a fullstop (**.**) or a question mark (**?**) to finish the sentences.

    (a) How old are you ▢   (b) I live in a blue house ▢

    (c) Which one do you want ▢

Going fishing

Going fishing

Dad said he would take me to the river and teach me how to fish.

He showed me how to put the bait on the hook, but the hook went into his finger.

So, I had to do it myself.

We put our lines in the water and waited.

I felt a tug on my line and I yelled to Dad.

He told me how to bring in the fish.

It was a very big one!

I put more bait on my line and put it back in the water.

I felt another tug and soon I had another fish.

We went home with ten big fish.

I caught all the fish.

I had a great day, but Dad didn't look very happy.

With your class

Talk about fishing.

* What do you need to take when you go fishing?

* Where can you go fishing?

* What do you need to do to catch a fish?

* What kinds of fish are there?

* Have you been fishing?

* Have you caught a fish?

* Why do you think Dad was unhappy?

With a partner

Tell your partner where you would like to go fishing and why.

Listen to your partner talk about fishing.

Draw where you would like to fish.

Use the recount on page 14 to complete the page.

1. Write the name of the recount.

_____

2. Where did the recount happen? _____

| at school | at home | at the river | at a party | in a boat |

3. Who was there?

_____

4. Write some of the things they did.

1. _____

2. _____

3. _____

4. _____

5. _____

5. Draw what happened at the end.

Read

1. Colour **yes** or **no**.

(a) Mum, Dad and the boy went fishing. .... (yes) (no)

(b) The boy caught 10 fish. .... (yes) (no)

(c) Dad caught two fish. .... (yes) (no)

(d) The boy was happy. .... (yes) (no)

(e) They went fishing at the river. .... (yes) (no)

(f) The fish were small. .... (yes) (no)

Read and think

1. Read the sentences and number them in the right order.

☐ The boy caught 10 fish.

☐ Dad put bait on his hook.

☐ They went to the river.

☐ Dad was sad.

☐ The boy felt a tug on his line.

2. (a) Why do you need to be careful when you put bait on a hook?

_____

_____

(b) Why did Dad have a sore finger? _____

_____

_____

Think

1. Finish the sentences.

   (a) I think the boy was happy because _____

   _____.

   (b) I think Dad was sad because _____

   _____.

   (c) I think _____ is the better fisherman because he

   _____.

2. (a) Draw a picture about what you think will happen next time they go fishing.

   (b) Finish the sentence.

   I think next time they go fishing _____

   _____

   _____.

All about words

1. Read the clue, finish the **er** words and draw a picture.

| river | father | water | mother | finger |

(a) She has children.

__ __ __ __ *e* *r*

(b) He has children.

__ __ __ __ *e* *r*

(c) A place to fish.

__ __ __ *e* *r*

(d) It's on your hand.

__ __ __ __ *e* *r*

(e) You drink it.

__ __ __ *e* *r*

2. Unjumble these words from the story.

(a) upt _____

(b) asdi _____

(c) vrye _____

(d) lal _____

(e) oson _____

(f) apyhp _____

3. **What am I?**

I am wet.

My skin is shiny.

I have fins.

I can swim.

I am a _____.

Draw me with my friends.

We can add **r** to all the vowel sounds to make new sounds.

a	e	i	o	u
 c**ar**	 f**er**n	 b**ir**d	 f**or**k	 ch**ur**ch

1. Make words using the middle sound and the letters around it. Draw pictures.

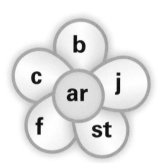

(a) _____

(b) _____

(c) _____

(d) _____

(e) _____

2. Read all the words. Circle the words with **er**.

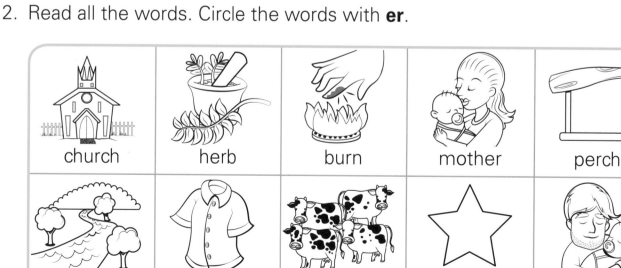

church	herb	burn	mother	perch
river	shirt	herd	star	father

3. Add **ir** to make words. Draw the pictures.

(a) b____ ____d

(b) d____ ____t

(c) sh____ ____t

(d) g____ ____l

(e) sk____ ____t

(f) th____ ____d

4. Read the words. Circle the **or** in each word.

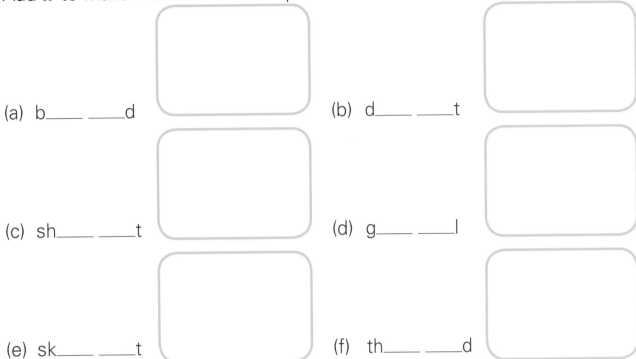

fork	short	corn	born	worn
storm	horn	port	morning	torch

5. Colour the boxes with the right words.

(a) Don't (**burn**) (**turn**) yourself.

(b) My rabbit has soft (**nurse**) (**fur**).

(c) I put money in my (**curl**) (**purse**).

(d) The boy fell and (**fur**) (**hurt**) his leg.

Nouns

Nouns are naming words for people, places and things.

1. Circle three places, underline three people and colour three things.

mum	home	teacher
ball	nest	beach
school	boy	cake

Pronouns

Pronouns take the place of a noun; for example: *I, me, she, he, you, it.*

2. Add a pronoun to each sentence.

(a)

_____ went to the beach.

_____ went too.

(b)

_____ walks to the park.

_____ walks to school.

(c)

_____ likes apples.

_____ likes them too.

(d)

My dog likes _____

because ____ feed _____.

(e)

_____ are my friend.

I play with _____.

(f)

_____ plays ball.

_____ can catch it.

1. Plan a recount about a trip with your dad or a friend.

TITLE: _____

ORIENTATION:

Where? _____

Who? _____

When? _____

Why? _____

EVENTS:

What happened?

CONCLUSION:

What happened at the end?

2. Write your recount on a sheet of paper and draw a picture.

After you finish writing, check these things to make your work better.

Writing

Has your recount got a name? .... ◯ **yes** ◯ **no**

Does it make sense? .... ◯ **yes** ◯ **no**

Did you leave out any words? .... ◯ **yes** ◯ **no**

Is it easy to understand? .... ◯ **yes** ◯ **no**

Are the events in the right order? .... ◯ **yes** ◯ **no**

Spelling

Did you check your spelling? .... ◯ **yes** ◯ **no**

Words

Did you think of interesting words to use? .... ◯ **yes** ◯ **no**

Punctuation

Did you put a capital letter at the start of every
sentence? .... ◯ **yes** ◯ **no**

Did you write people's names with a
capital letter? .... ◯ **yes** ◯ **no**

Have you used a capital letter for **I**? .... ◯ **yes** ◯ **no**

Did you remember full stops? .... ◯ **yes** ◯ **no**

1. Add **ar** to make words.

   (a) p＿＿ ＿＿k   (b) st＿＿ ＿＿   (c) f＿＿ ＿＿m   (d) c＿＿ ＿＿

2. Circle the **er** words.

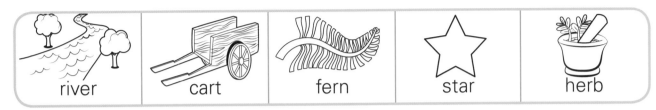

   river   cart   fern   star   herb

3. Add **ir** to make words.

   (a) g＿＿ ＿＿l   (b) b＿＿ ＿＿d   (c) sh＿＿ ＿＿t   (d) d＿＿ ＿＿t

4. Circle the **or** sound in the words.

   h o r n   p o r t   s h o r t s   f o r k   c o r n

5. Colour the box with the right word.

   (a) I (fur)(hurt) my finger.

   (b) My toy is soft and (furry)(turn).

   (c) She has a new (purse)(burnt).

   (d) My mother is a (purse)(nurse).

6. Circle the place noun, underline the people noun and colour the thing noun.

   school   toy   doctor

7. Add pronouns.

(a)

My dog has a ball.

＿＿＿＿ plays with ＿＿＿＿.

(b)

Mum is baking a cake.

＿＿＿＿ will eat ＿＿＿＿.

Talking in class

Talking in class

I think we should all be allowed to talk in class, but our teacher just won't let us. She gets really mad if we talk in her class, even when we're talking about schoolwork. This isn't fair.

The main reason we come to school is to learn. I think we can learn lots by talking to other people. We can tell them what we know and what we think, and listen to what they know and think. Then when we talk about things together, we can learn more.

My brother's teacher lets them do 'Think, pair, share' all the time. They get to sit knee to knee, looking at each other. First they think about the topic by themselves, then they talk about it with their partner. After that, they share some of their ideas with another group or with the whole class. He says it's great and he learns lots.

Just sitting and listening to your teacher all day isn't a good idea. I start to think about many other things. So I stop listening and I stop learning. It's just a waste of time and I get into trouble when I can't answer the teacher's questions. But when I have to talk I need to think, and that's good.

We should use our eyes, our ears and our tongues when we learn. And if we're not supposed to talk, why have we all got tongues?

All teachers must let us talk. If your teacher is like my brother's, you're lucky. But if you have a teacher like mine, ask if you can talk more in your class.

With your class

Talk about what happens in classrooms.

- When should children talk in class?

- When should they be quiet?

- Why can't you make lots of noise in a classroom?

- Is listening or talking more important?

- How do you know if someone is listening?

- What do good listeners do?

- What do good speakers do?

1. Draw you talking in your classroom.

With a partner

Tell your partner about your drawing, who you are speaking to and what you're talking about.

Listen to your partner tell you about his or her drawing.

Use the exposition on page 26 to complete the page.

TITLE:

1. Write the name of the exposition.

PURPOSE:

2. What does the writer want to happen?

ARGUMENTS:

3. Why does the writer think talking in class is a good thing to do?

_____

_____

_____

_____

_____

_____

_____

_____

CONCLUSION:

4. All teachers must _____

_____

_____.

Read

1. **Yes** or **no**? Colour the correct answer.

(a) The writer's teacher likes people talking in
her class. .... (yes) (no)

(b) The writer thinks talking in class helps
you to learn. .... (yes) (no)

(c) The writer would like to do 'Think, pair, share'. .... (yes) (no)

(d) The teacher knows when the writer isn't
listening because she can't answer her questions. ... (yes) (no)

(e) The writer has a brother. .... (yes) (no)

Read and think

1. Do you think the writer would like to be in your classroom? [ ]

Why/Why not? _____

_____

_____

2. Would you like to do 'Think, pair, share'? [ ]

Why/Why not? _____

_____

_____

3. Write one reason why talking in class isn't a good idea.

[ ]

Think

Plan a poster about talking in class. Write a list of dos and don'ts.
Make your poster and draw some pictures on it.

TALKING IN CLASS

Do	Don't

All about words

Some words look the same but have more than one meaning. They are called **homographs**.

1. Draw a picture to show another meaning for each word.

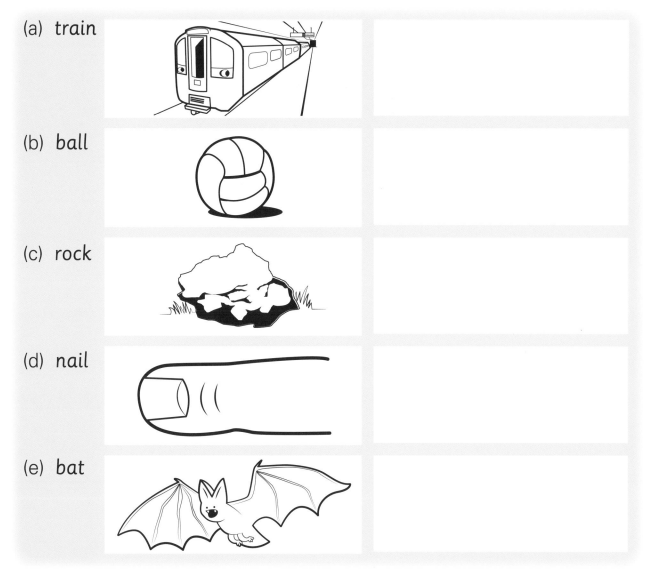

(a) train

(b) ball

(c) rock

(d) nail

(e) bat

2. Use these words to make a word shape. The first one has been done for you.

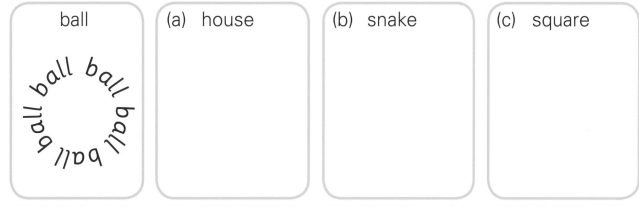

ball

(a) house

(b) snake

(c) square

Compound words are made up of two smaller words;
for example: *raincoat*.

3. (a) Join the words to make new words.

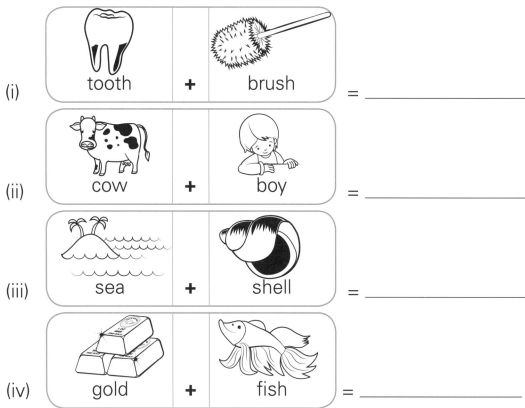

(i) tooth + brush = _____

(ii) cow + boy = _____

(iii) sea + shell = _____

(iv) gold + fish = _____

(b) Split these compound words, then draw a picture of the compound word.

(i) fireplace = _____ + _____

(ii) strawberry = _____ + _____

(iii) homework = _____ + _____

(iv) upstairs = _____ + _____

(v) scarecrow = _____ + _____

1. Add **ou** to make words. Draw pictures.

   (a) h____ ____se

   (b) m____ ____th

   (c) r____ ____nd

   (d) cl____ ____d

   (e) sh____ ____t

   (f) gr____ ____nd

2. Circle the **ow** word in the sentence, then write it at the end.

   (a) I fell down the stairs. _____

   (b) He has brown eyes. _____

   (c) The clown was very funny. _____

   (d) I will feed the cow. _____

3. Read the words. Write them. Draw pictures.

ball	tall	small	call	wall

4. Use an **oo** word in each sentence.

   (a) I can c____ ____ ____ with eggs.

   (b) L____ ____ ____ where you are going.

   (c) I read my b____ ____ ____ today.

   (d) Dad chopped the w____ ____ ____.

5. Choose **aw** or **or** to finish these words. Draw pictures.

(a) p___ ____

(b) l___ ____n

(c) cl___ ____

(d) f___ ___k

(e) s___ ____

(f) sh___ ____t

(g) c___ ___n

(h) sp___ ___t

(i) st___ ___m

(j) j___ ____

6. Circle the **au** sound in these words.

| sauce | August | pause | laundry | applaud |

7. Find the **alk** words in the word search.

| talk |
| walk |
| chalk |
| stalk |
| walking |
| talked |

w	b	k	l	a	t	b
v	a	m	k	n	d	k
r	e	l	d	e	g	l
q	a	d	k	n	o	a
w	p	l	c	i	h	t
c	a	m	f	j	n	s
t	k	l	a	h	c	g

8. Clap these words. How many syllables (parts) can you hear?

(a) teacher

(b) together

(c) themselves

(d) partner

(e) tongue

(f) brother

Conjunctions

Conjunctions are joining words. They can join words, ideas or sentences; for example: *I eat pears **and** apples.*
*My dog is short, **but** not fat.*
*We waited **because** the bus was late.*

1. Fill in the missing joining words.

    (a)    knife _____ fork

    (b) 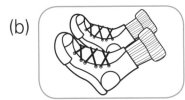   shoes _____ socks

    (c)    He likes brown _____ yellow,

    _____ not black.

    (d)    Mum slowed down _____ she saw the dog.

2. Tick (✓) the best word to join these sentences. Rewrite each sentence.

    (a) My friend is pretty. She is kind.   ○ **and** ○ **but** ○ **as**

    _____

    (b) My cat eats chicken. It doesn't eat fish.   ○ **and** ○ **but** ○ **as**

    _____

    (c) We looked carefully. We crossed the road.   ○ **and** ○ **but** ○ **as**

    _____

1. Plan an exposition saying that whiteboards are better than blackboards and chalk.

TITLE: _____

INTRODUCTORY STATEMENT:

What do you think?

ARGUMENTS:

(Make a list starting with the strongest one.)

_____

_____

_____

_____

_____

_____

_____

_____

_____

_____

_____

CONCLUSION:

2. Write your exposition on a sheet of paper and draw a picture.

After you finish writing, check these things to make your work better.

Writing

TITLE: _____

INTRODUCTORY STATEMENT:

Did you state what the topic was?.................................○ **yes** ○ **no**

Did you say what you thought about it?...........................○ **yes** ○ **no**

ARGUMENTS:

Did you explain your ideas clearly?................................○ **yes** ○ **no**

Did you start with your strongest one? ....○ **yes** ○ **no**

CONCLUSION:

Did you say what you thought at the end?.......................○ **yes** ○ **no**

Spelling

Did you check your spelling? ....○ **yes** ○ **no**

Words

Did you think of interesting words to use? ....○ **yes** ○ **no**

Punctuation

Did you put a capital letter at the start of
every sentence?...○ **yes** ○ **no**

Have you used a capital letter for **I**? ....○ **yes** ○ **no**

Did you remember full stops?...○ **yes** ○ **no**

Have you used question marks? ....○ **yes** ○ **no**

1. Add **ou** to make words. Draw pictures.

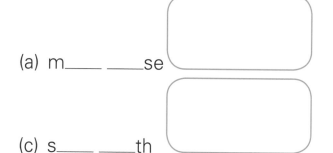

(a) m_____ _____se

(b) s_____ _____nd

(c) s_____ _____th

(d) sh_____ _____t

2. Circle the **ow** word in the sentence, then write it at the end.

(a) I will do it now. _____

(b) The town was quite small. _____

(c) The king wears a crown. _____

(d) Can you see the owl in the tree? _____

3. Read the words. Write them. Draw pictures.

hall	ball	small

4. Use an **oo** word in each sentence.

(a) I t_____ _____ _____ my books home.

(b) We st_____ _____ _____ up to sing.

(c) My f_____ _____ _____ is smaller than yours.

(d) The windows sh_____ _____ _____ as the truck went past.

5. Choose **aw** or **or** to finish these words. Draw pictures.

(a) j____ ____

(b) c____ ____n

(c) t____ ____n

(d) pr____ ____n

6. Circle the **au** sound in these words.

saucepan   **pause**   **laundry**

7. Clap these words. How many syllables (parts) can you hear?

(a) another

(b) partner

(c) mine

(d) question

(e) altogether

(f) school

8. Join these sentences using **and**, **but** or **as**.

(a) We stopped. The truck passed.

_____

(b) I like tomatoes. I like carrots.

_____

(c) He is big and strong. He isn't mean.

_____

Prince Hal and the dragons

Prince Hal and the dragons

Once upon a time in a far-off land there lived a young prince. Every day, Prince Hal went into the mountains by himself to explore the rocks and streams. No-one worried about him because he was brave and strong and he always came home before dark.

One day he found a cave hidden in the rocks. There was a strange noise and some smoke coming from the cave. At the back of the cave Hal found a young dragon sitting alone and roaring sadly. Prince Hal went up to him and asked why he was sad. The dragon said he was lonely. And that was the start of their friendship. With Hal on his back, the dragon went to faraway places. They had a great time.

One day the king told Hal that it was time for him to become a knight. Hal had to learn to fight with a sword. In spring his father told him he had worked hard and he was ready to slay his first dragon. Villages had been attacked and people had been killed by dragons. But there was one dragon Hal knew he would never slay.

The next day Hal was riding his horse in the mountains. A huge dragon appeared. It knocked him off his horse with its enormous tail. Grabbing his sword, Hal got up and moved towards his enemy. Hal kept fighting bravely even when he was tired and hurt. Then he dropped his sword. Just as the dragon was coming to finish him off, Hal's sword came flying through the air. His friend had suddenly appeared and he had flicked the sword to him with his tail.

Hal used all the strength he had left to kill the dragon. His friend then gently carried him back to the castle. The people were happy their prince was alive. The evil dragon wouldn't be troubling them again.

With your class

Talk about fairytales.

- How do they start?

- How do they finish?

- What are some of the characters?

- Are they true?

- What are dragons like?

- Are they real?

1. Draw a dragon.

With a partner

Tell your partner about the dragon you drew. How is it the same and how is it different from Prince Hal's dragon?

Listen to your partner tell you about the dragon he or she drew.

Use the story on page 40 to complete the page.

1. TITLE: _____

ORIENTATION:

2. (a) Who is the story about? _____

(b) Where was Prince Hal when the story happened?

_____

COMPLICATION:

3. (a) What was Hal's dragon's problem?

_____

(b) What problem did Hal have with the other dragon?

_____

EVENTS:

4. (a) What happened at the beginning of the story?

_____

(b) What did Hal have to do after he learned how to fight?

_____

RESOLUTION:

5. (a) How did Hal's dragon fix his own problem?

_____

(b) How did Hal fix the problem with the other dragon?

_____

ENDING:

6. Draw the ending.

Read

1. Colour **yes** or **no**.

   (a) Hal's dragon was in a cave. .... yes   no

   (b) Prince Hal went out looking for dragons to slay. .... yes   no

   (c) Hal had a sword. .... yes   no

   (d) Hal's dragon helped him when he was fighting. .... yes   no

   (e) The people were sad when Hal killed the dragon. ... yes   no

Read and think

1. Do you think Hal's dragon was kind?   yes   no

   Why/Why not?

   _____

   _____

   _____

2. Why are dragons' tails dangerous?

   _____

   _____

   _____

3. Why do you think Hal and his dragon were such good friends?

   _____

   _____

   _____

Think

1. Draw the pictures.

Hal's dragon	**Prince Hal**

2. Think about Hal's dragon and the dragon that attacked him.

   Make lists of things that are the same and different.

The two dragons in the story	
Same	Different

All about words

Similes

A simile says one thing is like another;
for example: *He is as busy as a bee.*

1. Use the words below to finish the similes.

bat	night	owl	ice	feather	snow

(a) as cold as _____

(b) as white as _____

(c) as blind as a _____

(d) as wise as an _____

(e) as light as a _____

(f) as black as _____

2. Match the things with their colours.

grass •   • grey

sky •   • white

chocolate •   • red

sun •   • purple

elephant •   • pink

snow •   • brown

tomato •   • yellow

grapes •   • orange

carrot •   • green

tongue •   • blue

3. Sort these words into alphabetical order.

| knight | sword | dragon | prince | cave | fight |

_____

_____

_____

4. Some words are either masculine or feminine. Complete this table.

Masculine	Feminine
king	
	princess
man	
	girl
father	
	daughter
uncle	
grandfather	

Silent letters

Two consonants placed together can sometimes make one sound; for example: **gn**ome, **kn**ife.

1. Read, circle the two consonants making one sound, copy and draw.

lamb	half	palm	comb	knight

knot	calf	knee	climb	thumb

2. Use one of these words to complete each sentence.

knew	calm	numb	gnocchi	limb	knock

(a) I had to _____ loudly on the door.

(b) The sea was very _____ today.

(c) She _____ all the answers.

(d) My tooth was _____ after I went to the dentist.

(e) His mum makes tasty _____.

(f) A heavy _____ broke off the tree in the storm.

3. Unjumble these words. Draw pictures.

(a) mogne _____

(b) btmhu _____

(c) tonk _____

(d) efkin _____

(e) enke _____

(f) mcbli _____

Plural means more than one. Most words just add **s** to show more than one; but words ending in **s**, **ss**, **sh**, **ch** and **x** need to add **es** to make them easier to say.

4. (a) Read the words. Add **es** to make plurals. Read the new words.

(i)   box___ ___   (ii)   bus___ ___   (iii)   cross___ ___

(iv)   wish___ ___   (v)   lunch___ ___   (vi)   boss___ ___

(vii)   fox___ ___   (viii) beach___ ___   (ix)   dish___ ___

(b) Many words ending in **o** also add **es** to make a plural form.

Read the words. Add **es** to make plurals. Read the new words.

(i)   tomato___ ___   (ii)   hero___ ___   (iii)   potato___ ___

(iv)   echo___ ___   (v)   buffalo___ ___

(c) Lots of music words ending in **o** only add **s**; for example: *duos, trios*.

Add **s** to these.

(i)   piano___   (ii)   banjo___

(iii)   soprano___   (iv)   cello___

(v)   radio___   (vi)   video___

Adjectives

An adjective is a describing word. Adjectives make your writing more interesting. They are used to describe nouns.

1. Use an interesting adjective for these nouns.

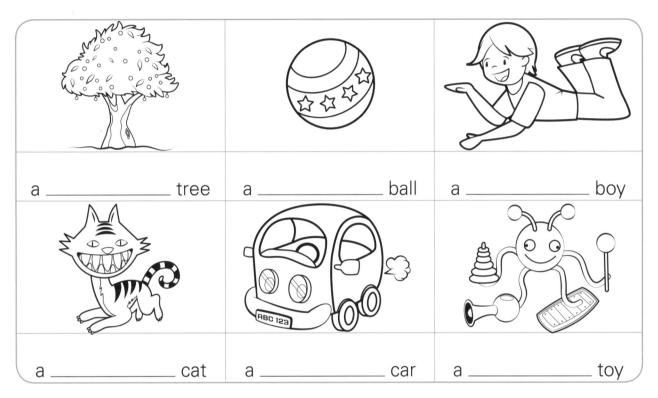

a _____ tree   a _____ ball   a _____ boy

a _____ cat   a _____ car   a _____ toy

2. Match the adjectives with their opposites.

heavy •   • small

far •   • cold

ugly •   • tall

big •   • light

short •   • dry

wet •   • happy

hot •   • near

sad •   • beautiful

Direct speech

When we write words that have been said, we put quotation marks, around these words; for example: *'I'm going home now', Mary said.*

3. Put in the quotation marks needed below.

(a) Stop! called the police officer.

(b) Can you help me? asked Mum.

(c) Welcome back! my friend shouted.

(d) Tom whispered, Can you see it?

(e) The boy yelled, Come back here!

4. If we use a speech bubble, we don't need quotation marks. Complete the conversation.

John

Can we please go to the zoo?

Jack

Dad

1. Plan a narrative about an animal nobody wants.

TITLE:

My story is called _____.

ORIENTATION:

Who is the story about?

_____

Where are they?

_____

When did it happen?

_____

COMPLICATION:

What was the problem?

_____

_____

EVENTS:

What happened?

_____   _____

_____   _____

_____   _____

RESOLUTION: ENDING:

How was the problem fixed?   How did the story end?

_____   _____

_____   _____

_____   _____

2. Write your story.

After you finish writing, check these things to make your work better.

Writing

TITLE: _____

ORIENTATION: Did you say who was in the story?............ ○ **yes** ○ **no**

Did you tell when it happened? .... ○ **yes** ○ **no**

Did you tell where it happened? .... ○ **yes** ○ **no**

COMPLICATION AND EVENTS:

Did you say what the problem was?.................... ○ **yes** ○ **no**

Did you tell what happened? .... ○ **yes** ○ **no**

RESOLUTION AND ENDING:

Did you say how the problem was fixed? .... ○ **yes** ○ **no**

Did you tell what happened at the end? .... ○ **yes** ○ **no**

Spelling

Did you check your spelling? .... ○ **yes** ○ **no**

Words

Did you use interesting words? .... ○ **yes** ○ **no**

Have you used good describing words? .... ○ **yes** ○ **no**

Punctuation

Did you put a capital letter at the start of
every sentence?... ○ **yes** ○ **no**

Did you write people's names with a capital letter?.......... ○ **yes** ○ **no**

Have you used a capital letter for **I**? .... ○ **yes** ○ **no**

Did you remember full stops?.. ○ **yes** ○ **no**

1. For each word, circle the two consonants making one sound, copy and draw.

thumb	knot	gnome

2. Use one of these words to finish each sentence.

half   **climb**   **know**

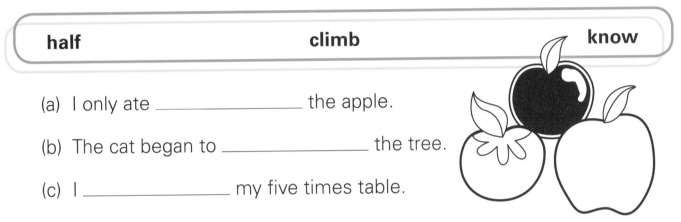

(a) I only ate _____ the apple.

(b) The cat began to _____ the tree.

(c) I _____ my five times table.

3. Unjumble these words. Draw pictures.

(a) blma _____

(b) acfl _____

4. Make plurals of these words.

(a) box_____   (b) cross_____   (c) lunch_____

(d) wish_____   (e) bus_____   (f) bush_____

5. Add **es** or **s** to these words to make plurals.

(a) tomato_____   (b) potato_____   (c) piano_____

(d) banjo_____   (e) echo_____   (f) radio_____

6. Add an interesting adjective to these nouns. Draw pictures.

a _____ dog	a _____ flower	a _____ girl

7. Match the adjectives with their opposites.

low •   • slow

fast •   • high

happy •   • sad

8. Put in the quotation marks needed below.

(a) Slow down , his friend called.

(b) Bob asked, Where are you going?

9. Complete the conversation below.

Where are you going?

Ice-cream

Ice-cream

Ice-cream is a sweet frozen dessert or treat.

Ice-cream is usually made from dairy products such as cream and milk. Most ice-creams have some sugar.

The word 'ice-cream' is sometimes used for frozen custards, yoghurts and sorbets.

Nobody really knows who made the first ice-cream. The Roman emperor, Nero, used snow and ice to cool and freeze fruit drinks. Marco Polo bought back recipes for frozen ices from the Far East. King Charles I of England served a sweet, creamy, frozen dessert and tried to keep it a secret so it was served only to royalty.

Nearly everyone loves ice-cream. It can be served in many ways and with many toppings. Ice-cream comes in many flavours.

Ice-cream can be eaten anywhere and at any time.

I like ice-cream. My favourite is chocolate. What's yours?

With your class

Talk about the ice-cream you like best.

- What does it look like?

- What does it taste like?

- What does it smell like?

- What does it feel like?

- Where do you get it?

- How is it served?

With a partner

1. Draw the best ice-cream ever. Choose three flavours and three toppings. Show how you would serve it.

2. Make up a name for your ice-cream.

    (a) I would call my ice-cream _____.

    (b) It would taste _____.

3. Tell your partner all about your ice-cream. Listen to your partner talk about his or her ice-cream.

Use the report on page 55 to complete the page.

1. TITLE: _____

CLASSIFICATION:

2. What is it?

DESCRIPTION:

3. Ice-cream is usually made from dairy products such as _____

and _____.

4. Three people we believe helped to give us ice-cream are:

The Roman _____ Nero,

Marco _____ and

King _____.

5. Ice-cream can be served in many _____ with many

_____.

6. Ice-cream comes in many _____.

CONCLUSION:

7. Ice-cream can be eaten _____ and at any _____.

I like _____.

Read

1. Join the sentences from the text.

    Ice-cream is •

    Most ice-creams •

    Ice-cream comes •

    I like •

    Ice-cream can be •

    • in many flavours.

    • ice-cream.

    • a sweet frozen dessert.

    • eaten anywhere.

    • have some sugar.

Read and think

1. Why can't you keep ice-cream in a cupboard?

    _____

    _____

    _____

2. Explain how ice-cream got its name.

    _____

    _____

3. Nero could only have his special treat in winter. Explain why.

    _____

    _____

4. Why do you think King Charles I wanted to keep his frozen dessert a secret?

    _____

    _____

Think

1. Read these facts about ice-cream. Tick the box to show what you think.

   (a) It takes about 50 licks to lick
       away one scoop of ice-cream. .... ⃝ **interesting** ⃝ **not interesting**

   (b) Most ice-creams are bought
       on Sundays. .... ⃝ **interesting** ⃝ **not interesting**

   (c) Children from ages 2 to 12 and adults
       over 45 eat the most ice-cream. .... ⃝ **interesting** ⃝ **not interesting**

   (d) Five per cent of people share their
       ice-cream with their pets. .... ⃝ **interesting** ⃝ **not interesting**

   (e) The USA has a national ice-cream
       month in July. .... ⃝ **interesting** ⃝ **not interesting**

   (f) The most popular ice-cream
       flavour is vanilla. .... ⃝ **interesting** ⃝ **not interesting**

   (g) Chocolate syrup is the most
       used topping. .... ⃝ **interesting** ⃝ **not interesting**

   (h) People eating ice-creams
       sometimes get a 'brain freeze'. .... ⃝ **interesting** ⃝ **not interesting**

2. Make up a new flavour of ice-cream.

   My flavour will be _____.

   Plan a poster to tell everyone about your ice-cream. Make it colourful.

All about words

Ice-cream is a compound word—a word made with two smaller words. Many foods are compound words.

1. Join up the words to make foods. Draw them.

straw •   • fruit

pine •   • kin

grape •   • root

beet •   • berry

pump •   • apple

mush •   • room

2. Put these ice-cream flavours into alphabetical order.

strawberry chocolate lime banana caramel vanilla neapolitan

_____

_____

_____

3. We have five senses: taste, touch, smell, hearing and sight.

    Put these words about ice-cream under their right sense. Some words can be used twice.

colourful	nice	round	sticky	white
tasty	minty	delicious	sweet	soft
crunch	yummy	melty	cold	slurp

sight	hearing	smell	touch	taste

4. Find the words in the ice-cream word search.

sweet	cone
yummy	scoop
ice-cream	soft
flavour	topping
milk	nuts
sugar	tasty

t	o	p	p	i	n	g	y
e	f	o	t	s	a	b	m
m	s	o	f	t	y	a	m
i	t	c	j	t	e	x	u
l	u	s	s	r	m	q	y
k	n	a	c	o	n	e	p
g	t	e	e	w	s	n	o
h	c	u	r	a	g	u	s
i	r	u	o	v	a	l	f

1. (a) Read these words and listen to the sound the beginning letter **c** makes.

cut	cent	can	circle	cycle
call	cart	centre	cell	craft	cat
celery	cake	cyclone	circus	count

(b) Sort the words into the right boxes.

c as in **kite**

_____

_____

_____

_____

_____

_____

_____

c as in **ice**

_____

_____

_____

_____

_____

_____

_____

(c) Which three letters after **c** make it sound
like the **c** in **ice**? .... ◯, ◯, ◯

2. (a) Look at these words.

ace   face   pace   trace   grace   lace   place   race   space

(b) Circle the **ace** sound.

(c) Complete these words using the **ace** sound and draw pictures.

ƒ_____	r_____	l_____	sp_____	tr_____

3. (a) Read these words and listen to the sound the letter **g** makes.
   G can make the **g** sound as in **gate** or a **g** sound as in **age**. Circle the
   words with the **g** sound as in **age**.

goat	gentle	giant	gun	game
gym	gave		germ	group
great	gypsy	grab	ginger	go

(b) Which three letters after **g** make it sound
   like the **g** in **age**?... ⬜ , ⬜ , ⬜

4. (a) Look at these words and circle the **age** sound.

   age   cage   page   wage   rage   stage   engage

(b) Use one of the words to finish each sentence.

   (i)   My bird lives in a _____.

   (ii) I coloured in the _____.

   (iii) My sister's _____ is six.

   (iv) We acted on the _____.

Plural means more than one.

Most plurals just add **s** – *cats, trees, dogs, bikes*.

Words ending in **f** or **fe** change the **f** to **v** and add **es**;

for example: *elf – elves, knife – knives.*

5. Write the plurals of these words.

   (a) wife _____   (b) wolf _____

   (c) life _____   (d) calf _____

   (e) half _____   (f) shelf _____

Prepositions

Some words tell us about the **position** of things.

These words are called **prepositions**;

for example: *in, under, on, over, inside.*

1. Underline the preposition in each sentence. Complete the picture.

(a) A man is standing inside the van.

(b) A little dog is behind the boy.

(c) A tree is near the garden.

(d) Two birds are flying over the tree.

(e) An ice-cream sign is above the window.

(f) A lady is between the van and the garden.

1. Plan a report about chocolate.

TITLE: _____

CLASSIFICATION:

What is it?

DESCRIPTION:

What does it look like?

_____

_____

_____

_____

How is it made?

_____

_____

_____

How is it used?

_____

_____

_____

CONCLUSION:

What do you think about chocolate?

2. Write your report and draw a picture.

After you finish writing, check these things to make your work better.

Writing

Has your report got a name?.. ◯ **yes** ◯ **no**

Does it make sense?.. ◯ **yes** ◯ **no**

Did you leave out any words? .... ◯ **yes** ◯ **no**

Is it easy to understand? .... ◯ **yes** ◯ **no**

Are the events in the right order? .... ◯ **yes** ◯ **no**

Spelling

Did you check your spelling? .... ◯ **yes** ◯ **no**

Words

Did you use interesting words? .... ◯ **yes** ◯ **no**

Punctuation

Did you put a capital letter at the start of every
sentence?.. ◯ **yes** ◯ **no**

Did you remember full stops? .... ◯ **yes** ◯ **no**

Have you used commas for lists? .... ◯ **yes** ◯ **no**

1. (a) Read the words and listen to the sound the letter **c** makes.

cart	**city**	**call**	**cub**
cent	**cell**	**cut**	**celery**

(b) Sort the words into the right boxes.

c as in **kite**	**c** as in **ice**
_____	_____
_____	_____
_____	_____
_____	_____

2. Complete the words using the **ace** sound and draw the pictures.

pl_____	sp_____	tr_____

3. (a) Read the words and listen to the sound the letter **g** makes.

go	**giant**	**giraffe**	**goat**
gave	**germ**	**great**	**gum**

(b) Circle the words with a **g** as in **age** sound.

4. Complete the sentence using an **age** word.

(a) What is your _____?　　(b) I read up to p_____ 66.

(c) There are two birds in the c_____.

5. Write the plurals of these words.

(a) elf _____　　(b) knife _____　　(c) wolf _____

Humpty Dumpty biscuits

This procedure explains how to do something.

Read these instructions for making Humpty Dumpty biscuits.

Humpty Dumpty biscuits

You will need:

oval-shaped biscuits

Smarties® (or M&M's®)

icing sugar

jelly beans

chocolate sprinkles

water

food colouring (pink)

a bowl

a spoon

a knife

Steps:

1. Place the icing sugar in a bowl.

2. Add water and mix with a spoon until just runny.

3. Add a little food colouring and mix.

4. Spread the icing over the biscuits.

5. Dip into the chocolate sprinkles for his hair.

6. Decorate with Smarties® (eyes and nose) and a jelly bean mouth.

7. Enjoy!

With your class

Think about learning to make a sandwich.

- Brainstorm the equipment or materials you require for this task and list them.

- Discuss what you need to do first and write it.

- Work together to determine the remaining steps.

- Discuss how you will know you have been successful.

With a partner

1. With a partner, draw then discuss your favourite cake or biscuit.

   Decide who will be the speaker and who will listen. Take turns.

Speaker	**Listener**
Tell the listener:	Ask the speaker anything else you would like to know about his/her favourite cake or biscuit.
• the name of your favourite	
• where it comes from	
• what is in it	
• how it smells	
• what it tastes like.	

2. Did you find it easier to be a speaker or listener?   ◯ **speaker**   ◯ **listener**

   Why? _____

   _____

   _____

Use the procedure on page 68 to complete the page.

1. TITLE: _____

GOAL:

2. The procedure tells you how to _____

_____.

NEEDS:

3. Draw and label the things you will need.

STEPS:

4. How many steps are there? [ ]

5. Write the beginning word of each step.

1. _____

2. _____

3. _____

4. _____

5. _____

6. _____

7. _____

These word are all doing words.

TEST:

6. How would you know if the procedure was right?

_____

Read

1. **Yes** or **no**? Colour the correct answer.

   (a) You mix in the water with a spoon. .... (yes) (no)

   (b) The chocolate sprinkles make a beard. .... (yes) (no)

   (c) A jelly bean is the mouth. .... (yes) (no)

   (d) The icing sugar is in a cup. .... (yes) (no)

   (e) You ice the biscuit before you decorate it. .... (yes) (no)

Read and think

1. These biscuits would be easy to make. (yes) (no)

   Why/Why not? _____

   _____

2. Why do you think the biscuits are called Humpty Dumpty biscuits?

   _____

   _____

3. Would younger or older children
   enjoy these biscuits?

   [   ]

   Why do you think this? _____

   _____

   _____

   _____

Think

Make a poster to tell people about Humpty Dumpty biscuits. It should be bright and colourful. Use words like **yummy**, **delicious**, **sweet** and **tasty**.

All about words

1. Cross out every second letter to make words from the procedure.

    (a) b p i r s t c x u b i c t d s i   _____

    (b) c l o b l d o f u s r t i u n x g y   _____

    (c) d t e r c s o y r f a e t y e g   _____

    (d) s b p d r e i t n s k f l g e i s r   _____

2. Unjumble the mixed-up words from the story.
   Use the starting letter as a clue.

    (a) poson   s_____   (b) fienk   k_____

    (c) gniic   i_____   (d) tmohu   m_____

3. Complete the crossword using the picture clues.

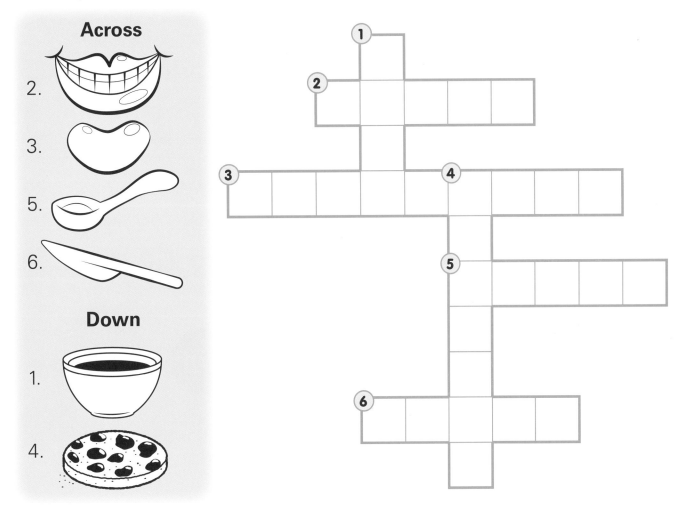

Across

2.

3.

5.

6.

Down

1.

4.

Magic e

Magic **e** can be added to words to change a short vowel sound to a long vowel sound.

For example: *rat/rate, pet/Pete, bit/bite, rod/rode, cub/cube*

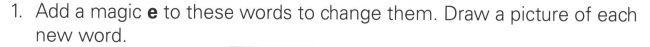

1. Add a magic **e** to these words to change them. Draw a picture of each new word.

(a) mat _____

(b) rob _____

(c) tub _____

(d) fin _____

(e) can _____

(f) not _____

(g) cut _____

(h) pin _____

(i) man _____

(j) rid _____

2. Circle the pictures with a long vowel sound.

Long vowels

When two vowels go walking, the first one does the talking and says its name;

for example: *oa (boat)*, *ai (train)*, *ea (bean)*, *oe (toe)*, *ie (pie)*, *ue (blue)*.

3. Read the words. Write the long vowel sound. The first one has been done for you.

(a) rail   `a`   (b) road ⬜   (c) bead ⬜

(d) hoe   ⬜   (e) goat ⬜   (f) due   ⬜

(g) tied   ⬜   (h) main ⬜   (i) feed ⬜

4. Unjumble the words with long vowels. The pictures will help you.

(a) lita _____      (b) otad _____

(c) aset _____      (d) eti   _____

(e) bteu _____   (f) medra _____

(g) nria _____      (h) ispe _____

Verbs

Procedures use words to tell us what to do.

These words are called **verbs**. They describe an action.

1. Circle all the verbs (doing words) in the list of actions. The first one has been done for you.

(a)

(Cleaning) your teeth	Writing a letter
Putting on your shoes	Riding a bike
Watching TV	Skipping with a rope
Reading a book	Climbing a tree

(b) Work with a partner. Mime one of the actions and ask your partner to guess what you are doing.

(c) Give your partner a turn to mime.

(d) How many actions did you guess correctly?

(e) How many actions did your partner guess correctly?

(f) Which action was the easiest to guess? _____

Command verbs give orders.

2. Write six command verbs from the procedure.

P_____   A_____   S_____

Di_____   De_____   E_____

3. Draw a picture to tell what could be happening.

Hurry!	Stop!

Adverbs

Adverbs can tell more about the verb. An adverb tells us HOW, WHEN or WHERE the action happened. Adverbs make our writing more interesting. A lot of adverbs end in **ly**;

for example: *Climb slow**ly**. Think careful**ly**.*

1. Add an **adverb** to tell **how** the action was done. The first one has been done for you.

   (a) Run ___quickly___

   (b) Throw _____

   (c) Talk _____

   (d) Watch _____

2. Add an **adverb** to tell **when** the action happened. Choose one from the box.

today	always	later	never

   (a) We must _____ finish our work.

   (b) He is _____ late.

   (c) The class will make biscuits _____.

   (d) I go to bed _____ on Friday nights.

3. Circle the **adverb** which shows **where** the action happened.

   (a) The boy was playing outside.

   (b) Put the book there.

   (c) They camped nearby.

   (d) Last night I slept downstairs.

1. Plan a procedure to make a hamburger.

TITLE: _____

GOAL:

What do you want to do?

_____

NEEDS:

STEPS: Put your steps in order.

1. _____

_____

2. _____

_____

3. _____

_____

4. _____

_____

TEST:

How would you know if someone can follow your procedure?

2. Check your work.

After you finish writing, check these things to make your work better.

Writing

Has your procedure got a name? .... ○ **yes** ○ **no**

Does it make sense? .... ○ **yes** ○ **no**

Did you leave out any words? .... ○ **yes** ○ **no**

Are the steps easy to understand? .... ○ **yes** ○ **no**

Are the steps in the right order? .... ○ **yes** ○ **no**

Spelling

Did you check your spelling? .... ○ **yes** ○ **no**

Words

Did you use command verbs? .... ○ **yes** ○ **no**

Punctuation

Did you put a capital letter at the start of every
sentence? .... ○ **yes** ○ **no**

Did you remember full stops? .... ○ **yes** ○ **no**

1. Add a magic **e** to these words. Draw pictures for the new words.

(a) rod _____

(b) win _____

(c) not _____

(d) tub _____

(e) mat _____

(f) shin _____

2. Circle the pictures of things with a long vowel sound.

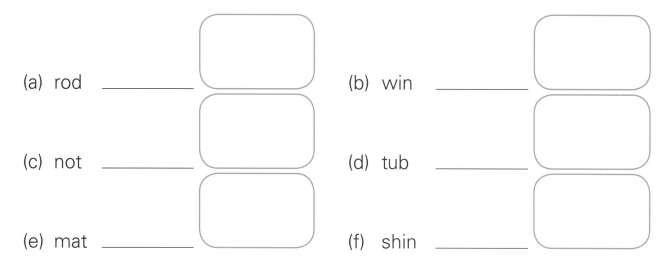

3. Read the words with long vowel sounds. Write the long vowel sound.

(a) float ⬚   (b) leaf ⬚   (c) train ⬚   (d) pies ⬚

4. Unjumble the words with the long vowels.

(a) stie _____

(b) tiab _____

(c) odla _____

(d) adrme _____

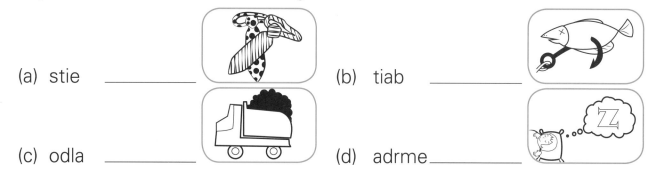

5. Circle all the verbs (doing words) in the list of actions.

    (a) Running after a ball

    (b) Sitting at a desk

    (c) Flying a kite

    (d) Meeting a friend

6. Add an **adverb** to tell **how** the action was done.

    (a) Walk _____

    (b) Hop _____

    (c) Read _____

7. Add an **adverb** to tell **when** the action happened.
Choose from the box.

tomorrow	later	now

    (a) It is going to rain _____.

    (b) You must do your work _____.

    (c) _____, we will play a game.

8. Circle the **adverb** which shows **where** the action was done.

    (a) My dog ran outside.

    (b) We live nearby.

    (c) He drove forwards.

Sleepover

Sleepover

Last week, my best friend, Owen, invited me to his house for a sleepover. I felt so happy. I ran all the way home to tell Mum my good news.

On Saturday morning, I helped Mum pack my bag. She put in some clean shorts and a T-shirt, some underwear and some socks, my pyjamas, my toothbrush and a comb. I picked up Stretch, my giraffe, and put him in the bag, too. Stretch is my favourite old toy and he always comes to bed with me.

My brother grabbed Stretch and pulled him out of my bag. He said that Owen would laugh at me if I took Stretch. He said Owen would think I was still a baby.

I put Stretch back on my bed. He looked very sad and I felt sad, too. What could I do?

It was great at Owen's. We played football at the park and had a swim. After that we had pizza for tea and we played some computer games. Then it was time for bed. I cleaned my teeth and just before I hopped into bed, I got Stretch and hid him under my pillow.

We talked and told jokes until Owen's mum said we had to go to sleep. She gave Owen a hug, and said goodnight to Floppy, his rabbit. She gave me a hug, then Stretch got one, too.

With your class

Talk about favourite toys.

- Why do children have toys?

- What makes some toys special?

- Are old toys better than new ones?

- Why do children take toys to bed with them?

- Is how toys look more important than how they feel?

1. Draw your favourite toy.

With a partner

Tell your partner about your toy. Why is it special? Where do you keep it?

Listen to your partner tell you about his/her favourite toy.

Ask questions about this toy.

Use the recount on page 82 to complete the page.

1. Write the name of the recount.

   _____

2. Where did the recount happen?

   _____

3. Who was in the recount?

   _____

4. Write some of the things that happened after Owen invited him for a sleepover.

   1. _____

   2. _____

   3. _____

   4. _____

   5. _____

   6. _____

   7. _____

   8. _____

5. Draw what happened at the end.

Read

1. What was the boy's friend's name?

2. What are three things he took with him to his friend's house?

    _____ _____ _____

3. What kind of animal is Stretch?

4. What did the boys do at the park?

    _____

5. Why did his brother take Stretch out of the boy's bag?

    _____

    _____

Read and think

1. (a) Do you think the boy's brother was trying to help him?

    (yes) (no)

    (b) Explain why you think this.

    _____

    _____

2. Where was Owen's toy rabbit? _____

3. Why do you think the boy hid Stretch under his pillow?

    _____

    _____

4. How do you think Owen's mum guessed Stretch was under the boy's pillow?

    _____

Think

1. What are some things you used to do when you were younger that you don't do now?

2. Complete the timeline.

   (a) When I was one, I learnt to _____

   _____.

   (b) When I was two, I liked _____

   _____.

   (c) When I was three, my favourite food was _____

   _____.

   (d) When I was four, my favourite toy was _____

   _____.

   (e) When I was five, I could _____

   _____.

   (f) Now I am ⬚, I like to _____

   _____.

All about words

1. Put these time words into alphabetical order.

week	morning	Saturday	night	after	before

_____

_____

2. Match the opposites.

before •   • dirty

night •   • sad

backward •   • cry

clean •   • never

asleep •   • after

happy •   • awake

always •   • forward

laugh •   • morning

3. Sort out these animals.

(a) tca _____

(b) odg _____

(c) hsroe _____

(d) rffigae _____

(e) barbit _____

(f) gtire _____

4. (a) **What am I?**   Draw me.

I am an animal.

I have a long neck.

I eat leaves.

I have spots.

I am a _____.

(b) **What am I?**   Draw me.

I am an animal.

I have long, floppy ears.

I have soft fur.

I live in a burrow.

I am a _____.

5. Make up your own animal 'What am I?'

What am I?

_____

_____

_____

_____

_____

I am _____.

MYSTERY ANIMAL

1. (a) Circle the **long a** sound in each word.

cake	train	rail	way	play
main	bake	mane	sail	lay
stay	name	hay	tail	gave

(b) Three ways to make the **long a** sound are ⬜ , ⬜ , ⬜ .

2. Put the right **a** sound in these words.

(a) c___v___   (b) p_____   (c) aw_____   (d) s___m___

(e) m_____l   (f) sn_____l   (g) w_____t   (h) l___k___

(i) cl_____   (j) pl_____n

There are different ways of making the **long e** sound; for example:

e (m**e**)   **ee** (tr**ee**)   **ea** (l**ea**f)   **ey** (k**ey**)   **y** (bab**y**)

3. Find and write a **long e** sound for each of the words.

(a) W___ went to the b_____ch yesterday.

(b) Sh___ could f_____l the *pupp*___ shaking.

(c) I have *thr*_____ brothers.

(d) My *bab*___ sister loves m___.

(e) Can you s_____ who is on the s_____t?

(f) Use the k_____ to open the door.

(g) The *sill*___ *monk*_____ climbed a *tr*_____.

(h) They will *cl*_____n the *gr*_____n car.

Most nouns (naming words) add an **s** to show plurals (more than one); for example: *cat – cats, dog – dogs.*

Some words are the same for singular (one) and plural.

4. Circle the plurals in these sentences.

   (a) I saw lots of sheep at the farm.

   (b) Many fish were in the pond.

   (c) Dad caught three trout.

   (d) At the zoo we fed all the deer.

Sometimes, whether there is only one thing or many of them, the plural word stays the same; for example: *shorts, tweezers.*

5. Choose one of the words below to finish each sentence.

   | jeans   pyjamas   scissors   binoculars   trousers   glasses |

   (a) I need my _____ to read.

   (b) You will need _____ to cut it out.

   (c) He watched the birds with his _____.

   (d) My sister's _____ had a patch on them.

   (e) Dad wore his new _____ to work.

   (f) I wore my _____ to bed.

Proper nouns

Some nouns give people, places or things a special name; for example: **M**r **S**mith, **C**oral **B**each and **N**intendo®. These are called proper nouns. They always start with a capital letter.

1. Use a proper noun to answer the questions.

   (a) What is your name?   _____

   (b) Who is your best friend?   _____

   (c) Where do you live?   _____

   (d) Where were you born?   _____

   (e) What is your favourite board game?   _____

   (f) What is your favourite TV show?   _____

2. Underline the proper nouns in these sentences.

   (a) Tom Brown was born in Ireland.

   (b) He lives in Dublin.

   (c) His favourite author is Roald Dahl.

   (d) His friend, Dick Jones, likes playing Monopoly®.

   (e) They like to visit Cork.

   (f) Their favourite place to eat is Joe's Pizzas.

3. Circle the pictures of proper nouns.

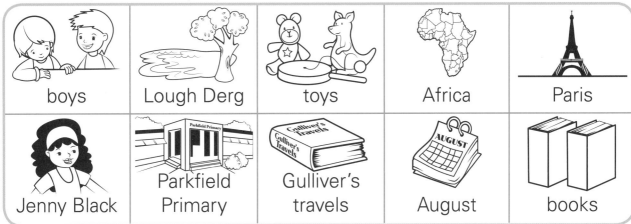

| boys | Lough Derg | toys | Africa | Paris |
| Jenny Black | Parkfield Primary | Gulliver's travels | August | books |

1. Plan a recount about a sleepover you have had or would like to have.

TITLE: _____

ORIENTATION:

    Where? _____

    Who? _____

    When? _____

    Why? _____

EVENTS:

What happened?

CONCLUSION:

What happened at the end?

2. Write your recount on a sheet of paper and draw a picture.

After you finish writing check these things to make your work better.

Writing

TITLE: _____

ORIENTATION:

Did you tell who was there? .... ○ **yes** ○ **no**

Did you tell when it happened? .... ○ **yes** ○ **no**

EVENTS:

Did you tell where it happened? .... ○ **yes** ○ **no**

Did you tell what happened? .... ○ **yes** ○ **no**

Were the events in the right order? .... ○ **yes** ○ **no**

ENDING:

Did you tell how it ended? .... ○ **yes** ○ **no**

Spelling

Did you check your spelling? .... ○ **yes** ○ **no**

Words

Did you use interesting words? .... ○ **yes** ○ **no**

Did you use any 'time' words? .... ○ **yes** ○ **no**

Punctuation

Did you put a capital letter at the start of
every sentence? .... ○ **yes** ○ **no**

Did you write people's names with a capital letter? .... ○ **yes** ○ **no**

Have you used a capital letter for **I**? .... ○ **yes** ○ **no**

Did you remember full stops? .... ○ **yes** ○ **no**

1. Circle the **long a** sound in each word.

> snake   rain   day   trail   bake   away   fake   play

2. Put the right **long a** sound in each word.

   (a) t___k___   (b) st_____   (c) pl___ ___n

   (d) w___ ___t   (e) m___k___   (f) tod___ ___

3. Find and write a **long e** sound for each of these words.

   (a) H___ has thr___ ___ toy cars.

   (b) My pupp___ likes to dig by the tr___ ___.

   (c) I saw a monk___ ___ swing on the bars.

4. Circle the plurals in each sentence.

   (a) I caught lots of fish today.   (b) We fed many sheep at the farm.

5. Choose a word below to finish the sentences.

> **pyjamas**   **jeans**   **glasses**

   (a) I found Mum's reading _____.

   (b) My _____ have stripes on them.

   (c) I fell over and tore my _____.

6. Use a proper noun to answer the questions.

   (a) What is your dad's name? _____

   (b) Where do you live? _____

7. Underline the proper nouns.

   (a) My friend lives in Clare Street.   (b) His birthday is in September.

Learn to swim

Learn to swim

I think everyone must learn to swim!

Hundreds of children and adults drown every year. Some of them fall into rivers and dams and lots of people drown in the sea and in swimming pools. A drowning can happen so quickly and so quietly that people don't even know it's happening. Some of these people's lives could have been saved if they had learnt how to swim.

You are never too old or too young to learn how to swim. My mum taught me how to swim before I could walk because she was so worried I'd fall into our pool and drown.

My grandma learnt how to swim in case one of us fell into the pool when she was looking after us. She says that if she could learn to swim, other old people can too.

Think about all the great things you can do if you're not frightened of water. Things like diving, sailing, fishing, surfing and canoeing. I think it's sad some people don't feel safe when they do these things because they can't swim.

Can you swim? If you can't, you must learn. This could save your life or someone else's life and you will be able to do lots of great water sports too.

With your class

Talk about:

- where you go swimming

- who you swim with

- learning to swim

- what swimming feels like

- why you like or don't like swimming

- things you enjoy doing on or in water.

With a partner

1. Draw something you can do or would like to be able to do in or on water.

2. Tell your partner about your drawing and why it is a great thing to do.

3. Listen to your partner talk about his or her drawing.

Use the exposition on page 95 to complete the page.

1.   TITLE: _____

PURPOSE:

2. The writer thinks that

ARGUMENTS:

3. • People should learn to swim because hundreds of _____

   and _____ drown _____ _____.

   • Lives would be saved if more people _____

   _____.

   • Very young people can _____.

   • Old people can _____.

   • If you are not frightened of water, you can _____

   _____.

CONCLUSION:

4. You must learn to swim. It could _____ your life

   or someone else's _____ and there are lots of

   _____ _____ _____ you can do too.

Read

1. Join the correct parts to make a sentence.

Lots of people fall into •   • in the sea and in pools.

Lives can be saved •   • learn to swim.

Babies can •   • if you're not frightened.

People can drown •   • if people learn to swim.

Water activities are fun •   • rivers and dams.

Learning to swim •   • saves lives.

Read and think

1. (a) Do you think the writer is a good swimmer?   (yes)   (no)

   (b) Why do you think this? _____

   _____

   _____

2. (a) Do you think the writer's mum thinks people should learn to swim?

   (yes)   (no)

   (b) How do you know this is what she thinks?_____

   _____

   _____

3. (a) Do you agree with the writer?   (yes)   (no)

   (b) Why/Why not? _____

   _____

   _____

Think

1. (a) Draw a picture of a water activity you would like to do.

(b) Do you need to swim to do this activity?   (yes) (no)

(c) What equipment do you need for this water activity?

(d) Why do you think this is a good activity?

_____

_____

Compound words

A compound word is a word made up of two smaller words;

for example: *raincoat, fireplace.*

1. (a) Match the words below to make compound words.

some •	• stairs
sail •	• shine
up •	• berry
to •	• one
play •	• boat
sun •	• crow
straw •	• time
scare •	• day

(b) Add words to make two compound words.

(i) foot _____   (ii) tooth _____

_____   _____

(iii) any _____   (iv) rain _____

_____   _____

2. Choose the correct word and circle it.

(a) We like to swim   (for)   (four)   fun.

(b) The   (son)   (sun)   is shining.

(c) I have   (one)   (won)   fishing rod.

(d) She has   (bean)   (been)   sailing before.

(e) I hurt my big   (toe)   (tow)   at the beach.

3. Match up the following water sports.

(a) | sw | vi | ing | _____

(b) | su | im | eing | _____

(c) | ca | il | ing | _____

(d) | di | no | ming | _____

(e) | fi | rf | ng | _____

(f) | sa | sh | ing | _____

4. Think of some words to describe how you feel when doing these activities.

(a) swimming _____ _____ _____

(b) fishing _____ _____ _____

(c) canoeing _____ _____ _____

(d) sailing _____ _____ _____

(e) surfing _____ _____ _____

1. Here are some ways to make the **long i** sound in words: **i–e**, **ie**, **y**.

   (a) Circle the **long i** sound in each word.

shine	spied	wide	try
my	lied	ride	fry
dry	bike	spy	tie
line	by	bite	dried

   (b) Choose the right **long i** sound for each word.

   (i)   h____d____   (ii)   cr____   (iii)   p____ ____

   (iv)   m____n____   (v)   tr____ ____d   (vi)   sp____

   (vii)   wh____   (viii)   l____k____   (ix)   l____ ____

   (c) Choose a **long i** word to complete the words in these sentences.

   (i)   Those book are m_____.

   (ii)   The river is very w_____.

   (iii)   The weather will be f_____ today.

   (iv)   She will d_____ into the water.

   (v)   I l_____ eating grapes.

   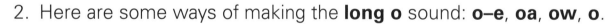

2. Here are some ways of making the **long o** sound: **o–e**, **oa**, **ow**, **o**.

   (a) Circle the **long o** sound in each word.

row	road	throw	so
throne	grow	toad	crow
no	rode	go	home
rose	goat	know	poke

(b) Circle the correct word.

(i)   I   (rode)   (road)   my bike to school.

(ii)   The tug will   (toe)   (tow)   the ship.

(iii) I   (know)   (no)   how to do it.

(iv)   My mum can   (sew)   (so)   well.

(v)   The queen sat on the   (thrown)   (throne).

Contractions

Sometimes two words can be put together to make a new, shorter word. This is called a contraction. A letter or letters may be taken out. An apostrophe shows where the letter(s) were;
for example: *we're = we + are.*

3. (a) Read each contraction and write the two words that make it.

   (i)   can't   = _____ + _____

   (ii)   he'll   = _____ + _____

   (iii)   couldn't   = _____ + _____

   (iv)   there's   = _____ + _____

   (v)   won't   = _____ + _____

   (b) Choose one of these contractions to complete each sentence.

Don't	**it's**	**Here's**	**won't**	**We've**

   (i)   I am feeling sick so I _____ come.

   (ii)   She thinks _____ a funny book.

   (iii) _____ your new cap.

   (iv)   _____ put your dish there.

   (v)   _____ seen that film before.

Plurals

If a word ends in **y** we change it to an **i** and add **es** to make plurals; for example: *fly – flies.*

4. Write the plurals of these words then draw pictures.

(a) baby _____

(b) daisy _____

(c) puppy _____

(d) try _____

(e) lolly _____

(f) spy _____

(g) bunny _____

(h) pony _____

(i) party _____

(j) berry _____

Exclamation marks

Exclamation marks show strong feelings;
for example: *Be careful!* *The floor is slippery.*

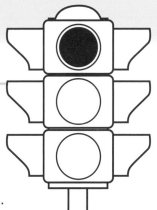

1. (a) Read the rhyme.

   'Stop**!**' says the red light.

   'Go**!**' says the green.

   'Wait**!**' says the amber light sitting in-between.

   (b) Read the rhyme again. Use strong feeling in your voice, then circle all
       the exclamation marks in the rhyme.

2. Add all the exclamation marks, then draw a mouth on each face to show
   how that person is feeling.

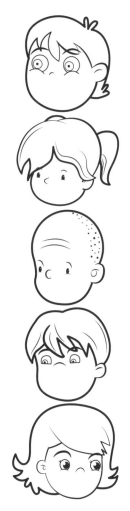

(a) Look out [ ] The train is coming.

(b) Help, Dad [ ] The boat is sinking.

(c) What a fantastic surprise [ ]

(d) Ouch [ ] I cut my finger.

(e) Oh no [ ] Here comes Mr Jones.

Conjunctions

Conjunctions are joining words. They join words or sentences together; for example: *I had peas **and** carrots.*

1. Read the rhyme and circle the joining words.

My special toy is ...

Red and white,

Shiny and bright,

Soft but strong,

Little but long,

Metal and wood,

Simple but good.

2. Fill in the missing joining words.

(a) bread _____ butter

(b) table _____ chair

(c) I can run _____ hop, _____ I can't skip.

3. Use **when**, **but** or **because** to join these sentences.

(a) My bike is old. It can still go fast.

_____

(b) I love my teddy. It is soft and cuddly.

_____

(c) He was playing on his computer. Mum called him.

_____

1. Plan an exposition titled 'Everyone should play sport'. Think of some good arguments.

TITLE: _____

INTRODUCTORY STATEMENT:

What do you want?

ARGUMENTS:

(Make a list.)

_____

_____

_____

_____

_____

_____

_____

_____

_____

_____

CONCLUSION:

2. Write your exposition on a sheet of paper and draw a picture.

After you finish writing your exposition, check these things to make your work better.

Writing

TITLE: _____

INTRODUCTORY STATEMENT:

Did you state what the topic was?.................................... ○ **yes** ○ **no**

Did you say what you thought about it?........................... ○ **yes** ○ **no**

ARGUMENTS:

Did you explain your ideas clearly?................................. ○ **yes** ○ **no**

Did you start with your strongest one?........................... ○ **yes** ○ **no**

CONCLUSION:

Did you say what you thought at the end?...................... ○ **yes** ○ **no**

Spelling

Did you check your spelling? .... ○ **yes** ○ **no**

Words

Did you think of interesting words to use? .... ○ **yes** ○ **no**

Punctuation

Did you put a capital letter at the start of
every sentence?... ○ **yes** ○ **no**

Have you used a capital letter for **I**? .... ○ **yes** ○ **no**

Did you remember full stops?.. ○ **yes** ○ **no**

Have you used question marks? .... ○ **yes** ○ **no**

1. Circle the **long i** sound in these words.

| tide | try | ride | fried | lie | my |

2. Use an **i–e** word to complete these sentences.

   (a) Mum will dr_____ us to the beach.

   (b) We l_____ up outside the classroom.

3. Circle the **long o** sound in these words.

| boat | groan | hope | tow | throw | moan |

4. Circle the correct word.

   (a) He (rode) (road) down the (rode) (road).

   (b) I (know) (no) that Mum will say (know) (no).

5. Write the two words that make these contractions.

   (a) we've = _____ + _____

   (b) he's = _____ + _____

   (c) don't = _____ + _____

   (d) she'll = _____ + _____

6. Write the plurals of these words.

   (a) party _____   (b) lolly _____

   (c) try _____

   (d) pony _____

   (e) spy _____

Our pets

Our pets

It was 'Pet Day' at the school
And all the pets were there.
Some with feathers, some with scales
And some with curly hair.

Then in walked Jake, the new boy,
With his 'pet' upon a lead.
And there was sudden silence,
No-one even breathed!

His pet was very ugly,
All teeth and tail and claws.
With green and leathery skin,
From its head down to its paws.

'My goodness', said the teacher,
'I hope your pet is tame.
It looks like it could bite me ...
Does it have a name?'

'Yes Miss,' said Jake, smiling,
'It's an African hairless terrier.
But it has another name
That I think is even scarier'.

'Another name? What might that be?'
The teacher asked with a smile.
'In Africa, where I come from, Miss,
It's called a crocodile.'

With your class

Talk about a pet you have or would like to have.

- What does this pet look like?

- What does it do?

- Why do you like it?

- How do you look after it?

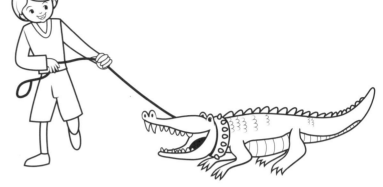

With a partner

1. (a) Draw your pet or the one you would like to have.

    (b) My pet's name is _____.

2. Tell your partner why you like this pet and some of the things your pet can do.

3. Think about all the things you need to do to look after your pet, then tell your partner the two that are the most important.

4. Listen to your partner talk about his or her pet.

Use the poem on page 110 to complete the page.

TITLE:

1. Write the name of the poem.

_____

ORIENTATION:

2. (a) Where did the story happen? _____

   (b) Who is the story all about?

   _____

   (c) Who else is in the story?

   _____

COMPLICATION:

3. (a) What was happening at school?

   _____

   (b) Why was the teacher scared?

   _____

RESOLUTION:

4. What did the teacher ask?

   _____

ENDING:

5. How did the story end?

Read

1. What colour was Jake's pet? _____

2. Did Jake's pet have a tail? (yes) (no)

3. Had Jake been at school for a long time? (yes) (no)

4. Where did Jake used to live? _____

5. What did Jake call his teacher? _____

Read and think

1. What was Jake's pet? _____

2. Why did they all stop talking when Jake arrived? _____

   _____

3. Was his teacher a man? (yes) (no)

4. (a) Do you think Jake's pet was ugly? (yes) (no)

   (b) Explain why you think this. _____

   _____

   _____

5. Why was the teacher scared of Jake's pet? _____

   _____

6. Why couldn't Jake's pet run away? _____

   _____

7. (a) Did some children bring birds to the pet day? (yes) (no)

   (b) How do you know? _____

   _____

Think

1. (a) Draw a scary pet. It doesn't have to be a real one.

(b) My pet is like Jake's pet because: _____

_____

_____.

(c) My pet is different from Jake's because: _____

_____

_____.

All about words

1. Join the rhyming words from the poem, then add one of your own.

paws •   • name   _____

there •   • might   _____

tame •   • scarier   _____

terrier •   • hair   _____

bite •   • claws   _____

2. (a) Draw and name an animal with scales.

(b) Draw and name three animals with hair.

(c) What pets are covered in feathers? _____

    Draw your favourite one.

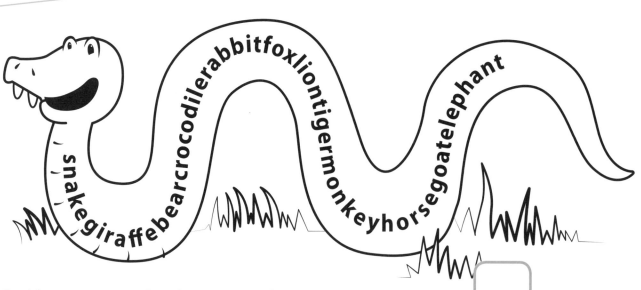

3. How many animals can you find in the word snake?

4. Unjumble these pets.

(a) smeou _____

(b) btarib _____

(c) gdo _____

(d) ttnike _____

(e) knaes _____

(f) grfo _____

(g) pyppu _____

(h) bdri _____

5. (a) Name two pets that live in water.

(b) Draw two pets that live in a cage.

There are different ways of making an **oo** as in **moon** sound:
ew, **ue**, **u–e**.

1. Read these words and circle the two letters which make the moon – **oo** sound.

| blue | true | glue | clue | untrue |

2. Add **ew** to these words.

(a) gr_____ _____   (b) cr_____ _____   (c) ch_____ _____   (d) scr_____ _____

(e) dr_____ _____   (f) br_____ _____   (g) thr_____ _____   (h) bl_____ _____

3. Fill in the **oo** sound and draw pictures.

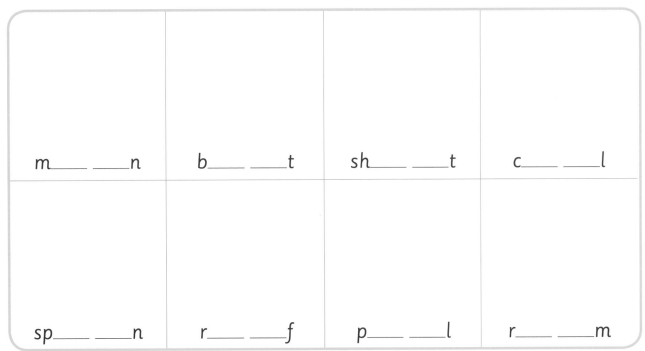

| m_____ _____n | b_____ _____t | sh_____ _____t | c_____ _____l |
| sp_____ _____n | r_____ _____f | p_____ _____l | r_____ _____m |

4. Use **air** or **ere** to complete these words.

(a) I sat on the ch_____ over th_____.

(b) Wh_____ did he put the p_____ of socks?

(c) Somewh_____ near the st_____s is my bag.

5. Spelling maths. Write the words then draw a picture.

(a) (**s**) + (**wa**) + (**n**) = _____

(b) (**wa**) + (**tch**) = _____

(c) (**wa**) + (**nd**) = _____

(d) (**s**) + (**wa**) + (**mp**) = _____

(e) (**wa**) + (**nd**) = _____

(f) (**wa**) + (**sh**) = _____

6. (a) Join the rhyming words.

bread •   • feather

ready •   • steady

weather •   • feathery

treading •   • head

leathery •   • spreading

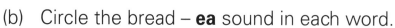

(b) Circle the bread – **ea** sound in each word.

7. Plural means more than one. Most words just add **s**. Some plurals change spelling. Write the plurals for these words.

(a) foot _____   (b) tooth _____

(c) child _____   (d) man _____

(e) goose _____   (f) person _____

Adjectives

Adjectives are used to describe nouns.

Using adjectives makes your writing more interesting.

1. (a) Find the words in the word search.

scary
ugly
curly
green
tall
leathery
hairless
new

t	b	y	r	e	h	t	a	e	l
a	q	c	q	s	r	t	n	a	e
l	r	l	u	g	l	y	t	u	b
l	s	u	r	r	v	d	n	e	w
t	n	e	c	f	l	h	k	g	c
r	e	t	t	b	w	y	e	h	k
n	m	s	s	e	l	r	i	a	h
s	c	a	r	y	e	d	s	f	g

(b) Choose one of the words to complete the sentence.

(i) The witch was very u_____.

(ii) My frog looked g_____ and l_____.

(iii) Mum has a n_____ car.

(iv) The h_____ dog looked s_____.

(v) She has very c_____ hair.

(vi) My brother is very t_____.

Comparing

When we compare two things, we can add **er**.
A boy is tall. His dad is taller.

When we compare more than two things, we can add **est**.
A worm is long. A lizard is longer. A snake is the longest.

2. Think of something to write in each space and draw a picture.

A _____ is big.

A _____ is bigger.

A _____ is the biggest.

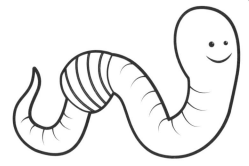

3. Fill in the missing words in the table.

(a)	high		highest
(b)		brighter	
(c)			warmest
(d)	poor		
(e)		darker	
(f)	small		
(g)		greener	
(h)			deepest
(i)	full		

1. Plan a narrative about a pet.

TITLE:

My story is called _____.

ORIENTATION:

Who is the story about?

_____

Where are they?

_____

When did it happen?

_____

COMPLICATION:

What was the problem?

_____

_____

EVENTS:

What happened?

_____   _____

_____   _____

_____   _____

RESOLUTION: ENDING:

How was the problem fixed?   How did the story end?

_____   _____

_____   _____

_____   _____

2. Write your story.

After you finish writing, check these things to make your work better.

Writing

Has your story got a name? .... ○ **yes** ○ **no**

Does it make sense? .... ○ **yes** ○ **no**

Did you leave out any words? .... ○ **yes** ○ **no**

Is it easy to understand? .... ○ **yes** ○ **no**

Spelling

Did you check your spelling? .... ○ **yes** ○ **no**

Words

Did you use interesting words? .... ○ **yes** ○ **no**
Have you used describing words? .... ○ **yes** ○ **no**

Punctuation

Have you got a capital letter at the start of
every sentence? .... ○ **yes** ○ **no**

Did you write people's names with a capital letter? .... ○ **yes** ○ **no**

Have you used a capital letter for **I**? .... ○ **yes** ○ **no**

Did you remember full stops? .... ○ **yes** ○ **no**

1. Circle the two letters which make the same sound as the **oo** in **moon**.

blue	**grew**	**moon**	**glue**
pool	**clue**	**blew**	**boot**
untrue	**soon**	**crew**	**true**
screw	**chew**	**loot**	**threw**

2. Use **air** or **ere** to complete these sentences.

   (a) I see a p_____ of socks over th_____.

   (b) Wh_____ are my f_____y books?

   (c) My sister has brown h_____ but mine is f_____.

   (d) Be careful you don't fall down the st_____s over th_____.

3. Spelling maths. Write the words then draw a picture.

   (a) **wa** + **nd** = _____

   (b) **s** + **wa** + **n** = _____

   (c) **wa** + **sh** = _____

   (d) **wa** + **tch** = _____

4. Join the rhyming words.

   feathery •   • treading

   bread •   • head

   ready •   • steady

   spreading •   • leathery

5. Write the plurals of these words.

    (a) foot _____

    (b) tooth _____

    (c) man _____

    (d) goose _____

6. Use one of the adjectives to complete the sentences.

curly	ugly	new	scary	leathery	green

    (a) I saw a s_____, g_____ frog.

    (b) My sister has c_____ hair.

    (c) The opposite of 'pretty' is 'u_____'.

    (d) The crocodile's skin was l_____.

    (e) My n_____ pet lives in a cage.

7. Fill in the missing words.

(a)	rich		richest
(b)		poorer	
(c)	light		
(d)		newer	
(e)			shortest
(f)	green		

Spiders

Spiders

Spiders are arachnids. 'Arachnid' is the Greek word for spider.

Spiders are not insects. They have two body parts (an abdomen and a thorax) and eight legs. They can grow a new leg if one is damaged. Spinning glands on their abdomens, called 'spinnerets', make the silk for their webs. Not all spiders spin webs.

The spider's skeleton is on the outside. It looks like skin and splits to let the spider grow.

Female spiders are usually larger than the males. Spiders are 'oviparous', which means they lay eggs. Baby spiders are called 'spiderlings'.

Spiders can be many colours and have been around for over two million years. They are found in almost every habitat in the world: from hot to cold and wet to dry.

The largest spider is the 'giant bird-eating spider' with a leg span of 28 cm. The tarantula is probably the most feared. The 'Brazilian wandering spider' is the deadliest spider and shoots venom through its fangs.

Many people are scared of spiders, but they eat insects and can be very useful by keeping harmful pests out of the garden.

Lots of poems, songs and stories have been written about spiders. Can you think of some?

The English workbook

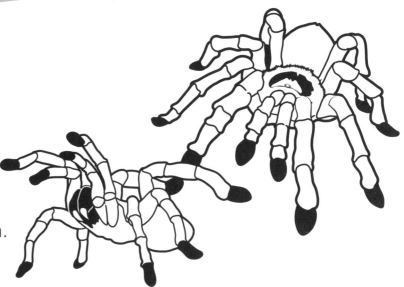

With your class

Talk about spiders:

- What they look like

- Where you've seen them

- What they do

- What you know about them.

With a partner

Tell your partner about a song, story or rhyme you know about spiders. Listen to your partner talk about his or her story, song or rhyme.

1. Draw a spider web with a spider in the middle.

1. TITLE:

What is the title?

2. CLASSIFICATION:

What are they?

_____

3. DESCRIPTION:

(a) What do they look like?

(b) Where do you find them?

(c) What can they do?

4. CONCLUSION:

Finish the sentences about the ending.

(a) Many people are scared of _____.

(b) They eat _____ and can be _____.

Read

1. Use a word from the box to finish the sentence.

> **female**   **two**   **skeleton**   **eight**   **male**

(a) Spiders have _____ body parts.

(b) Spiders have _____ legs.

(c) The spider's _____ is on the outside.

(d) A _____ spider is usually larger than a _____.

Read and think

Answer **yes** or **no**.

1. (a) A spider is an insect. .... yes   no

(b) Spiders lay eggs. .... yes   no

(c) Spiders are all one colour. .... yes   no

(d) Baby spiders are spiderlings. .... yes   no

2. Label the spider using these parts.

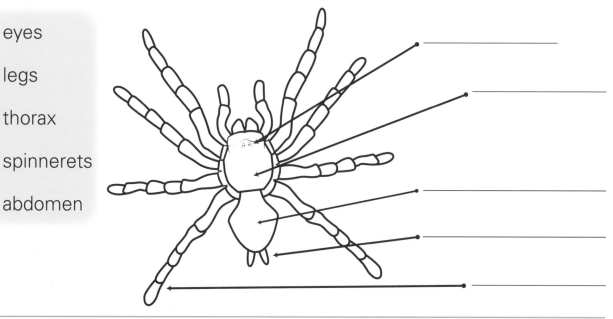

eyes

legs

thorax

spinnerets

abdomen

Think

Add these facts to the correct column.

Spiders	Insects	Both

8 legs	no antennae	can be useful
found in many places	no wings	6 legs
has antennae	different colours	2 body parts
usually small	can spin webs	can be harmful
usually have wings	3 body parts	many different types

All about words

1. Unjumble these words about spiders.

   (a) bwe _____   (b) gles _____

   (c) xotrha _____   (d) gesg _____

   (e) pdiers _____   (f) bbya _____

   (g) dnichraa _____ *(A tricky one!)*

2. Sort these animals into male and female.

cow	lion	**Male**	**Female**
billy	mare		
hen	nanny		
rooster	tiger		
ram	stallion		
tigress	bull		
ewe	lioness		

3. Put these spider words into alphabetical order.

   | legs   thorax   spinneret   abdomen   web   skeleton |

   _____

   _____

4. Join the opposites.

male •	• small
big •	• dry
hot •	• slow
wet •	• female
old •	• cold
fast •	• young

Tricky words

Some words can be tricky to spell because we can't sound them;
for example: *they, was, where, one.*

1. Learn and write these tricky words using:

| look | say | trace | cover | write | check |

	1st try	2nd try
was		
saw		
the		
they		
them		
one		
none		
done		
come		
some		
any		
many		

2. Which tricky word(s):

   (a) end with **y**?   _____   _____   _____

   (b) begin with **th**?   _____   _____   _____

   (c) have 3 letters?   _____   _____   _____

   _____   _____

Question words

Words that ask questions often begin with **wh**;
for example: *who, when, where, what, why.*

3. Use question words to fill in the spaces. Remember to start with **wh** and
   a capital letter.

   (a) _____ is your name?

   (b) _____ do you live?

   (c) _____ sits next to you?

   (d) _____ is your birthday?

   (e) _____ is your favourite colour?

4. Spelling maths

   (a) (**th**) + (**ey**) = _____

   (b) (**your**) – (**r**) = _____

   (c) (**s**) + (**ome**) = _____

   (d) (**d**) + (**o**) + (**n**) + (**e**) = _____

   (e) (**saw**) *backwards* = _____

   (f) (**none**) – (**n**) = _____

5. Write a sentence using a question word and a word from the spelling
   maths.

   _____

   _____

Prepositions

Some words tell us about the position of things. These words are called **prepositions**. These are words like ...

in, under, behind, inside, off, above, between, among.

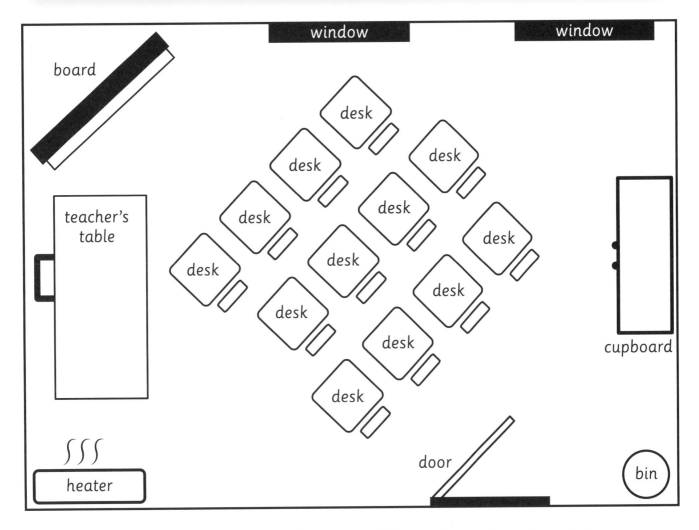

1. Read the sentences. Circle the prepositions. Complete the picture.

   (a) A boy is coming in the door.

   (b) A bag is by a window.

   (c) A box is under the board.

   (d) An apple is on the teacher's table.

   (e) Two chairs are next to the heater.

   (f) A toy box is between the windows.

   (g) The teacher is in front of the desks.

2. Choose a preposition from the box to finish the sentences.

by	with	around	through	up

   (a) Mum came _____ me to see the doctor.

   (b) We went to the zoo _____ train.

   (c) The boys ran _____ the field.

   (d) I looked _____ the window.

   (e) The dogs raced _____ the hill.

3. Write the opposite of these prepositions.

   (a) on   _____   (b) up   _____

   (c) in   _____   (d) inside _____

   (e) under _____   (f) before_____

4. Write a sentence using each preposition.

   (a) **above** _____

                        _____

   (b) **beside** _____

                        _____

   (c) **near** _____

                        _____

   (d) **off** _____

                        _____

1. Plan a report about an animal.

TITLE: _____

CLASSIFICATION:

What is it?

DESCRIPTION:

What does it look like?

_____

_____

_____

_____

Where do you find it?

_____

_____

_____

What can it do?

_____

_____

_____

CONCLUSION:

What do you think about it?

2. Write your report.

After you finish writing, check these things to make your work better.

Writing

Has your report got a title?... ○ **yes** ○ **no**

Does it make sense?... ○ **yes** ○ **no**

Did you leave out any words? .... ○ **yes** ○ **no**

Is it easy to understand? .... ○ **yes** ○ **no**

Have you written lots of facts?... ○ **yes** ○ **no**

Spelling

Did you check your spelling? .... ○ **yes** ○ **no**

Words

Did you use interesting words? .... ○ **yes** ○ **no**

Punctuation

Did you put a capital letter at the start of every
sentence?.. ○ **yes** ○ **no**

Did you remember full stops? .... ○ **yes** ○ **no**

Have you used commas for lists? .... ○ **yes** ○ **no**

1. Have a partner test you on these tricky words.

saw	was	they	one	none
come	some	any	many	them

How many did you get right? ⬜
Now test your partner.

2. Use a question word.

(a) _____ is your friend's name?

(b) _____ is at the door?

(c) _____ are you coming?

3. Spelling maths

(a) (**the**) + (**m**) = _____

(b) (**done**) – (**d**) = _____

(c) (**s**) + (**o**) + (**m**) + (**e**) = _____

4. Choose a preposition from the box to finish the sentences.

around	among	with	by

(a) I came to school _____ Mum.

(b) The dog ran _____ the tree.

(c) He was _____ the door.

(d) The bees flew _____ the flowers.

5. Read the sentences. Circle the prepositions. Complete the picture.

(a) A box is under the table.

(b) A dog is next to the cupboard.

(c) A girl is on the chair.

(d) A boy is between the table and the chair.

6. Write the opposite of these prepositions.

(a) off _____

(b) down _____

(c) outside _____

(d) above _____